OATS ARE FOR GOATS
AN EARLY READER SERIES
READER 3

Authors:
Annie Brown
Alpha Omega Staff

Alpha Omega
PUBLICATIONS

804 N. 2nd Ave. E.
Rock Rapids, IA 51246-1759

Instant Words

1.	the	he	go	who
2.	a	I	see	an
3.	is	they	then	their
4.	you	one	us	she
5.	to	good	no	new
6.	and	me	him	said
7.	we	about	by	did
8.	that	had	was	boy
9.	in	if	come	three
10.	not	some	get	down
11.	for	up	or	work
12.	at	her	two	put
13.	with	do	man	were
14.	it	when	little	before
15.	on	so	has	just
16.	can	my	them	long

17.	will	very	how	here
18.	are	all	like	other
19.	of	would	our	old
20.	this	any	what	take
21.	your	been	know	cat
22.	as	out	make	again
23.	but	there	which	give
24.	be	from	much	after
25.	have	day	his	many
26.	Tippy	wants	around	hurray
27.	table	mother	now	surprise
28.	too	father	ice cream	turtle
29.	every	school	house	Blackie
30.	apples	look	father	

Kelly's Daisies

It was finally spring.

Kelly couldn't wait until her family went camping. Every spring, they would go to Pine Lake for one week.

Pine Lake was so pretty. Green pine trees were everywhere.

Kelly loved the way the pine trees smelled. She liked to gather pine cones and look for wild flowers.

"Daisies are my favorite," she would tell her Mom and Dad. "They remind me of sunshine and make me smile."

Last year, Kelly wanted to pick some daisies to bring home. "They would look so pretty in my yellow vase," she thought. She asked her mom if it would be okay.

"Let's think about it," said Mom. "If everyone picked daisies to take home, what would happen?"

"There wouldn't be any for the next family to see," Kelly told her.

That gave Kelly an idea. She went to their tent and got her paper and paints.

"I'll paint a picture of the daisies," she said. "Then I will have them to look at everyday and so will others who come to Pine Lake."

Now, a year later, Kelly sat on her bed looking at her painting of the yellow and white daisies. They made her smile.

"The first things I will pack this year," she said to herself, "are my paper and paints."

Nonsense Poem

Take a rake,
stir a cake.

Bake a cake,
and eat the rake.

Jump in the lake,
wake a drake.

Shake the drake,
and drink the lake.

I Don't Know about Snow

Grandpa Jones comes down from Idaho in the wintertime when it begins to snow.

He packs his RV with everything he owns. From November to May, he'll call it his home.

He'll travel the road for two or three days, then arrive at my house for the long winter stay.

Grandpa said it used to be fun to play in the snow, sliding down hills and making snowballs to throw.

Now it's hard for him to get outside and shovel the walk. Grandpa says he'd rather sit with me in the sunshine and talk.

I hope someday, before I get old, I can go to Idaho and play in the snow.

Grandpa says it would be fun for me. But then, I really wouldn't know.

The Tree Fort

Lee has a tree fort.
It is up in a big green tree.
Dad helped Lee make the tree fort.
He and Lee sit in the tree house and talk.
Tippy jumps and jumps.
He wants to get up in the tree fort.

Mike's Light Bites

Mike likes eggs and milk.
He likes Light Bites the most.
His mom got these Light Bites last night.
She shops at Pike's.
Yum! Yum! Mom makes them just right!

A Tale of a Tail

The sky had been gray all week, but not today. The sun was shining bright, and James and Clay were ready to go sailing with their friend, Captain Raymond. They had been waiting all summer.

"It's a great day to go sailing," said Captain Raymond. "We might even see the whales as they swim south for the winter."

"Hurray!" shouted the boys. They quickly got water bottles and a small lunch.

James grabbed his notebook, and the boys raced to the dock.

"Climb in, boys, and put your life jackets on," yelled the captain. "We're ready to go."

It was easy sailing out of the bay into the sea. The waves were calm today.

The boys spent most of the time looking at the sea. They liked watching the seagulls dive for fish, but most of all they hoped to see a whale.

The day went fast, and it was getting late. Captain Raymond said it was time to go back.

"We haven't seen a whale yet," cried James.

"Maybe next time," replied Captain Raymond.

As the captain turned the boat toward the bay, the boys heard a big "swish" and a "splash."

James and Clay looked behind them just in time to see a large tail dip below the waves. They looked at each other and smiled big smiles. They had seen their whale after all, even if it was only its tail.

James grabbed his notebook and wrote: "Today I saw a whale. It was only the tail of a whale, but it was a great tail. That's the end of my tale."

Adam and Eve

Adam woke to a bright day.
Eve was by his side.
Adam and Eve rose to see plants and trees.
The sun was not hot.
Life was grand!

Oats Are for Goats

"Oh no! Not oats again!" groaned Grodin.
"I am not a goat who likes to eat oats."

So Grodin wrote a note and nailed it to the post. It read: NO OATS FOR THIS GOAT.

But every day, Grodin only got oats for breakfast, lunch, and dinner.

One day when no one was home, Grodin broke out of his pen and began to roam. "I will find something better than oats," he thought.

"Ah, ha!" he said, as he spotted the gray trashcan by the workshop.

"I know I will find something in there that is better than oats."

He was so excited he jumped up on all four legs.

PLOP! Down he came with a thud.

Picking himself up, he trotted over to the trashcan as fast as he could.

Grodin poked and poked around the can. He stuck his nose inside and found an old rope, a broken boat, a box of notes, and a bottle of soap.

"This has to be better than oats," he said, and he gobbled them all up.

"Oh, ohhhhhhh! I don't feel very well," groaned Grodin as he walked slowly back to his pen.

He groaned all night long.

The next morning, Grodin got oats again.

This time, he didn't say anything. He just gobbled them up. He even took his note off the post.

"Maybe I am a goat who should only eat oats," he sighed.

Clean Machine

Vroooooooooooooooooooooooom! goes the clean machine.

It picks up the papers
and sweeps the floor.

Vroooooooooooooooooooooooom! goes the
clean machine.

It picks up my clothes
and washes the door.

Vroooooooooooooooooooooooom! goes the
clean machine.

It dusts the tables
and scrubs the walls.

Vroooooooooooooooooooooooom! goes the
clean machine.
It stacks the dishes
and vacuums the hall.

Vroooooooooooooooooooooooom! goes the
clean machine.

I think it's time to pull the plug,
and give the "clean machine"
a great big HUG.

The Ball Game

Playing ball is fun.
Ray bats the ball.
Then he runs around the bases:
first base,
    second base,
        third base,
            home!
Ray hits a home run.
        Hurray for Ray!

Just Like Jesus

Before Tony goes to sleep at night, he always chooses a book to read. Sometimes he reads with his mom and dad. Other times, he reads alone.

Tonight Tony is going to read alone. He chooses the Bible and climbs into his bed. He gets under his blanket and puts his pillow behind his head. Now he is cozy and ready to read.

Tony reads about Jesus praying in the garden. Jesus got on His knees and prayed to God. He asked God to give Him strength.

While Tony was reading, his dad peeked in to say goodnight.

"Dad," Tony asks. "Why did Jesus have to pray when He is God?"

"Well," Dad replied, "Jesus prayed to God so we would know how to pray. He is our example."

"Oh," said Tony, thinking about what his dad had said.

Dad smiled, gave Tony a hug and kiss goodnight, then turned out the light.

Before Tony went to sleep, he got out of his cozy bed. He kneeled on the floor and prayed to God just like Jesus.

Jack's Table

Jack's table is red.
But Jack wants a blue table.
"I'll paint my table," he said.

Jack gets some blue paint.
He paints and paints.
He paints his table blue.
"Look, Mother," said Jack.
"I don't have a red table.
Now I have a blue table."

Lion Fun

The lions sit in the sun.
They will turn and gaze at a bird.
They will watch a turtle.
They will see a mother walking with her child.
They will not surprise the bird.
They will not jump at the turtle.
They will not scare the mother
    walking with her child.
They will sit still.
They like the soft grass.
They will curl up for a nap.

Rose's Rose

Rose's mother came home.

"Here is your surprise," said Mother.

"Oh, oh!" said Rose. "What is it?"

"It's a rose," said her mother,

"A red rose for my girl."

"Oh, thank you, Mother," said Rose.

"This rose is my very own.

My name is Rose, and I have a rose.

So this rose is Rose's rose!"

Working

All of us have work to do.
Fathers go to work every day.
Mothers work at home.
Some mothers go to work, too.

I work, too.
I work at school.
I can do good work.

I work at home.
I help my mother in the house.
I work with my father in the yard.

The Cross

"Why did the people nail Jesus to the cross?" Jeffrey Michael asked his mother.

"They nailed Jesus to the cross because they didn't understand Him," she replied.

"Was He mean?" Jeffrey Michael asked.

"No, He wasn't mean," she told him. "Jesus was trying to teach the people about God and love. He wanted them to love one another."

"Isn't that a good thing?" Jeffrey Michael asked, feeling confused. It didn't make sense to him that people would do such a mean thing to Jesus. It was hard to understand.

"Yes, love is a good thing," answered Mother. "God is good in all ways. He is so good that He forgives us when we do wrong things. He even forgave the people who nailed Jesus to the cross."

Fun with Words

A tree has bark on it.
A dog can bark.
Ice cream is cold.
You can catch a cold.
You can train your dog.
You can ride on a train.
Can you think of others?

That Buzzing Sound

"Look! There's a nice place under the old oak tree to play our game," said Lin Sue.

"You're right!" said Janie May. "The grass is soft, and there is shade from the hot sun."

Lin Sue and Janie May laid a blanket under the shade of the old oak tree. They took out their checker game and got ready to play.

"You can be red, and I'll be black," said Lin Sue. "You're my guest so you get to go first."

Just as Janie May was getting ready to move her first checker, the girls heard a buzzing sound.

"What is that buzzing sound?" asked Janie May.

"I don't know," said Lin Sue, "but I'm going to find out."

The girls ran to the workshop. Lin Sue's dad was cutting wood with his new saw. It made a buzzing sound, but not the same sound the girls had heard.

Then Janie May spotted a bee. They followed it to the peach tree in Lin Sue's backyard. They saw a busy beehive.

It made a buzzing sound, but not the same sound the girls had heard.

The girls heard the sound again near the front door of Lin Sue's house. When they went inside her mother was just taking a pan of cookies out of the oven. "Mmmmmm," the girls said at the same time.

Lin Sue's mother smiled and gave the girls a plate of cookies to take back outside.

"Mmmmmm, these cookies taste good," said Janie May. "I'm sure glad we found that buzzing sound."

I Like Stripes

I like stripes.
I like a zebra's stripes
that are white and black.

I like the brown and orange stripes on a tiger's back.

I like the red and white stripes on a popcorn bag.

I like the same color stripes on our American flag.

I like the rainbow stripes on a lollipop. I like the stripes on the cookies at the baker's shop.

I like the wide, purple stripes on my brand new dress.

I like anything with stripes, you might have guessed.

Big Blue

Do you know what animal is bigger than any other on the earth? Maybe you think it's a dinosaur that roamed the earth long ago. Some dinosaurs were very big, but this animal is bigger than any of the dinosaurs and is still alive today.

The biggest animal to ever live on the earth is the blue whale. It can weigh one hundred tons and grow to be one hundred feet long. That is longer than three buses!

Blue whales do not have any teeth. They have hundreds of thin strips in their mouth called "baleen." They eat tons of a tiny fish called krill which get trapped in the baleen.

Blue whales are not mean animals. They are rarely seen because they live in the deep sea, and there aren't very many left.

Man used to hunt blue whales for their blubber. Now it is against the law to kill the whales.

Maybe someday you will see a whale. Maybe it will be a blue whale— the biggest animal ever to live on the earth.

Jesus Prays

Our Father which art
in heaven,
Hallowed be thy name.
Thy kingdom come.

Thy will be done in earth,
As it is in heaven.
Give us this day our daily bread.
And forgive us our debts,
As we forgive our debtors.
And lead us not into temptation,
But deliver us from evil:
For Thine is the kingdom,
And the power, and the glory,
Forever, Amen.

A Sea Horse Is a Fish

Maybe you've heard of a catfish. It has long whiskers like a cat.

Maybe you've heard of a toadfish. It has a flat body and wide mouth like a toad. It's easy to think of these animals as fish. They have *fish* in their names and look like fish.

Maybe you've heard of a sea horse and wondered if it was a little horse that lived in the ocean. It doesn't have *fish* in its name, and it doesn't look like a fish.

But a sea horse is a fish. It has gills and fins like other fish. If you look closely, you can see how it got its name. Its small head looks very much like a horse's head.

If you look at the sea horse even more closely, you might think of other animals. It has a pouch to carry its babies. It has a long tail which can wrap around seaweed or swing from weed to weed. It has a hard, bony outer covering and can change colors to blend with rocks, wood, or plants.

A sea horse may look and act more like other animals, but now you know that a sea horse is really a fish.

My Little Black Pony

I have a little black pony.
I call him Blackie.

Blackie eats the green grass.
He likes apples, too.
Apples and green grass are good for him.

Blackie and I go for a ride.
We go fast.
We go all around the yard.

We have lots of fun.

A Sea Horse Is Not a Race Horse

"I'd like to be a race horse," said Peter. "I would run like the wind and win the big race."

"I'd like to be a sea horse," said Cindy. "I would swim all over the ocean and see whales, seals, and fish of all kinds.

"No you wouldn't," replied Peter.

"Why not?" said Cindy. She did not like Peter telling her she couldn't swim all over the ocean. This was her dream.

"You would have to be a very good swimmer to go all over the ocean," said Peter. "I just read a book about sea horses. It said sea horses are not good swimmers. They mostly drift about, letting the water move them. Sometimes they use the fin on their backs like a motor to move about, but they get tired very fast."

"Then I could drift all over the ocean. I don't care if it takes me a long time," said Cindy.

"The book also said sea horses stay close to home," replied Peter. "Instead of swimming all over the ocean, they spend most of their time sitting in the middle of seaweed or other plants. They wrap their long tails around a weed and sit. While they sit, they eat. In fact, sea horses eat all the time. They watch the other fish zip here and there grabbing their meal, but they can't move that fast. So, sea horses sit and eat the plants and small animals that come their way."

"Oh," said Cindy, sadly. "I guess I won't be a sea horse after all. It isn't much fun sitting all the time."

"You can still be a sea horse, Cindy," said Peter, trying to make her feel better. "Just think of all the interesting fish and sea creatures that would go by as you sat quietly in the seaweed. You could see them, but they wouldn't see you! I'm sure a whale or two would come your way and maybe even seals and sharks!"

"I don't know," said Cindy. "I think I'd rather be an octopus."